Swindon College

Contents

Introduction

Developing the skills of counting and writing numbers to 10

Children's first steps in learning to count often begin informally at home with their families. They come into contact with many numbers in their daily lives and start to rehearse counting by joining in with nursery rhymes, listening to stories such as 'The Three Little Pigs' and watching television programmes. They may also begin to experiment with counting when they are playing with their toys or helping out with familiar tasks at home.

By the time they reach four years of age, children of average ability and above are starting to draw pictures or marks on paper which represent numbers of objects. This may be a simple circle with two dots and two 'sticks' at the bottom of the circle representing a person, or a group of basic shapes or marks representing objects.

Numbers to 10 focuses on consolidating children's skills in counting and writing numbers to five and helping them to develop and practise skills in counting to 10 in a variety of different situations. The book aims to help children associate counting processes with written numbers and encourage them to recognize and practise writing numbers to 10. Children are introduced to placing written numbers in the correct order; the first principles of subtraction, through taking one object away from a small group of objects and counting the number of objects left; and addition, through counting numbers of objects in two small sets then counting to find the total.

Early Learning Goals

Numbers to 10 is for children who are reasonably confident with counting and writing numbers to 5, have experience of using

numbers in practical contexts to solve simple problems which involve counting and are ready to extend their skills to working with numbers to 10 and beyond.

This book provides a programme that helps children towards achieving the following Early Learning Goals for Mathematics identified by the Qualifications and Curriculum Authority (QCA):

- Say and use number names in order in familiar contexts.
- Count reliably up to 10 everyday objects.
- Recognize numerals 1 to 9.
- Find one more or one less than a number from 1 to 10.
- Begin to relate addition to combining two groups of objects, and subtraction to 'taking away'.
- Use developing mathematical ideas and methods to solve practical problems.

Baseline Assessment

All the activities in this book are planned to develop mathematical skills in young children that will enable them to achieve the Early Learning Goals for Mathematics by the end of the Reception year. This, in turn, will enable them to confidently tackle the baseline assessment tasks that they will be expected to carry out when they enter reception classes in mainstream schools.

How to use this book

The activities in this book are designed to be used flexibly according to the children's level of development. While there is a planned structure to the activities for average four-year-olds, consideration is also given to younger and older children with support and extension ideas. This book is specifically designed to offer activities to help children develop skills when working with numbers to 10. There are structured practical group and individual activities, games focusing on numbers 5 to 10 and photocopiable sheets to help children consolidate their skills of counting and writing numbers. Where the photocopiable sheet is to be used by individual children, the activity is referred to as an 'Individual recording' and can be kept for assessment purposes. If the sheet is to be used by a group of children, then it is referred to as an 'Individual task'. All the activities are adult directed and require the presence and interaction of an adult.

The Skills development chart at the back of the book is designed to help you incorporate the activities into your planning procedures. Ensure that adult helpers are pre-briefed about the activities and the preparation that is required beforehand.

Progression

Numbers to 10 introduces the first principles of subtraction through taking away one object from a small group of objects. Practical activities are provided for children to practise counting and writing the numbers 1 to 10 and explore and use the numbers 5 to 10 to solve simple problems involving counting.

As a final stage, children are asked to recognize that the numbers of objects in two sets are the same and also to count the numbers of objects in two small sets and find the total number. For younger or less able children, you may wish to use the first book in the series – *Numbers to 5* – which develops children's confidence and understanding of working with numbers up to five.

Finding out what children already know

Before you begin to plan your work, it is helpful to find out what the children already know. You can achieve this by:
● finding out how far a child can count orally
● checking how far a child can count objects correctly by touching them and saying the number
● checking how far a child can write numbers in a recognizable form
● finding out how many objects a child can count by sight without touching them
● counting out a small set of objects with a child, then adding one or two objects. Does the child tell you the number by counting the objects or is she able to work it out mentally?
● counting out a small set of objects with a child, then taking away one or two objects. Does the child tell you the number by counting the objects or is he able to work it out mentally?
Note: These assessment suggestions will not necessarily be appropriate for all children. It is up to you to decide which suggestions you should use. If a child is unable to confidently carry out the above activities with numbers up to and including 5, you may prefer to use the activities in the first book in the series – *Numbers to 5*.

Home links

At the end of each activity there are suggestions for how parents and carers can help their child at home. If you wish to involve parents, it is important to establish this principle at the beginning, and to ensure that parents receive appropriate guidance. This can be achieved informally through daily contact. If you are concerned about a particular child and wish parents to help their child with a specific skill, it is important that you share your ideas with the child's parents and invite their observations.

Ducks on the pond

Learning objectives
To recite the rhyme 'Five Little Ducks'; to trace numerals 0 to 5; to make a set of five then take away different numbers of objects and say how many are left.

Group size
Whole group game; small group activity for four to six children working with an adult.

What you need
A copy of the photocopiable sheet for each child; one copy of the sheet for the adult enlarged to A3 size and copied onto card; scissors; glue; colouring materials.

Preparation
Colour in the pond and the ducks on the large photocopied sheet. Laminate the card. Cut out the pond outline and the duck cards.

What to do
Sit in a circle. Say the rhyme 'Five Little Ducks' (from *This Little Puffin* compiled by Elizabeth Matterson, Puffin) inviting the children to do the actions. Choose five children to be the little ducks and one to be the mother duck. Recite the rhyme again, asking the mother duck to stay in the centre of the circle, or 'pond', while the five little ducks waddle around the outside. When you reach the line *Mother Duck said, 'Quack, quack, quack, quack'*, let the mother duck quack to her ducklings, then ask just four children to return to the centre.

Repeat the game with different children.

Individual recording
Place the five duck cards on the laminated pond. Ask the children in turn to make a duck 'swim away' by taking a card out of the pond, and then to count how many ducks are left. Replace the cards, then ask individuals to make two, three or four ducks 'swim away', counting how many are left each time.

Give each child a photocopied sheet. Ask them to colour in the pond and the ducks, then to carefully cut out the duck cards. Invite them to trace over the numbers at the top of the page, starting at the big dots and following the arrows.

Ask them to count the number of duck cards they have, and to write the number in the duck outline. Encourage the children to place all their ducks on the pond, then to remove one. Let them count how many are left and write the answer in the box on the right. Encourage them to complete the examples independently at their own pace. When they have finished, invite them to glue their ducks onto the pond.

Support
Demonstrate the activity using the laminated pond and ducks. Ask the children to copy you with their ponds. Ask them to count and say the number before writing it in the box. Scribe numbers in yellow marker for the children to trace.

Extension
Repeat the activity using extra duck cards to a number the children can comfortably count and write numbers to (up to 10).

Assessment
Note whether the child can take the correct number of ducks from the pond, then count and write the number left in the boxes.

Home links
Ask parents to show their child a set of 5 or more objects. Tell them to take different numbers of objects away from the set, then to ask their child to count and say how many are left.

Ducks on the pond

1 swims away

2 swim away

3 swim away

4 swim away

5 swim away

Flower game

Learning objectives
To recognize and say numbers thrown on a dice; to count and write numbers up to 6.

Group size
Two to four children working with an adult.

What you need
A copy of the photocopiable sheet for each child; a dice with spots from 1 to 6 and a shaker for each child; a tray; sets of coloured counters; pencils; crayons or felt-tipped pens.

Preparation
Draw spots in the squares on the flower petals to match the spot dice and photocopy the sheet for each child.

What to do
Give each child a shaker, a dice, a set of counters and a copy of the photocopiable sheet. Ask the children to take turns to throw their dice into the tray, then to say the number thrown. Challenge them to find the petal with the same number of spots on the flower and to cover the spots with a counter. The first child with a counter on each of the six flower petals is the winner. Let the children repeat the game several times.

Individual recording
After playing the game, ask the children to trace the numbers at the top of the sheet, starting at the big dots and following the arrows. Now ask them to draw six leaves on the stem of the flower, then write the number six on the flowerpot. Let the children colour in their flower picture.

Support
On the children's photocopiable sheets, write the numbers 1 to 6. Play the game with a number dice.

Extension
Write the numbers 1 to 6 in the squares on the children's photocopiable sheets, but play the game using a spotted dice. Challenge the children to match the spots to the numbers.

Assessment
Note whether the child can recognize and count the number of spots on a dice. Check that the child can count, write or trace numbers to six correctly.

Home links
Encourage parents to play simple board and dice games such as 'Beetle' or 'Ludo' with their child. Alternatively, give parents two or more copies of the Flower Game sheet to play with their child at home.

Flower game 123456

Egg boxes

Learning objectives
To practise counting to 6; to practise adding and subtracting from 6; to find different ways to arrange two eggs in a six-egg box.

Group size
Four children working with an adult.

What you need
A copy of the photocopiable sheet for each child plus one copy enlarged to A3 size; four six-egg egg boxes; Plasticine or playdough; crayons or felt-tipped pens; a small easel; marker pen.

Preparation
Attach the enlarged photocopiable sheet to a small easel.

What to do
Ask the children to each make two pretend eggs from Plasticine or playdough, roughly the size of real eggs. Place an empty egg box in the centre of the table and invite each child in turn to put one egg into the box. Ask 'How many eggs are there in the box?' each time. When the egg box has six eggs in it, invite each child in turn to take one egg out of the box. Ask 'How many eggs are left in the box?' each time.

When the children are familiar with the activity, alternate between inviting the children to put in one or two eggs each time and counting the total, then taking one or two eggs out and counting how many are left.

Individual recording
Sit at a table and place the easel and A3 sheet where everyone can see it. Place an egg box in the centre of the table. Invite a child to place their eggs in the egg box in any position they wish. Now ask the child to draw the eggs in the correct places in the first box on the A3 sheet, then to take their eggs out of the box. Ask the next child to put their eggs in the box in different positions, then to draw them in the second egg box. When all the children have taken a turn, give each child a copy of the photocopiable sheet and an egg box, and let them repeat the activity independently.

Support
Put the eggs together in a basket. Ask each child in turn to count out, for example three eggs, and put them in the egg box as they count them, then put them back in the basket. For the individual work, provide counters and show the children how to map out the position of the eggs in the boxes before drawing them.

Extension
Provide a second copy of the photocopiable sheet and challenge the children to find more ways of placing the eggs so that they are in different positions to the ones on the first sheet. (There are 15 possibilities!)

Assessment
Note whether the child is able to count the eggs by sight or whether he needs to touch each egg to count them. In the individual work, note whether the child is able to record the positions of the eggs on the sheet correctly.

Home links
Ask parents to try the activity at home with their child, finding as many ways as they can to arrange two small potatoes in an egg box. Ask parents to draw egg box diagrams on paper for their child to record the positions. Don't forget to tell them that there are 15 possibilities!

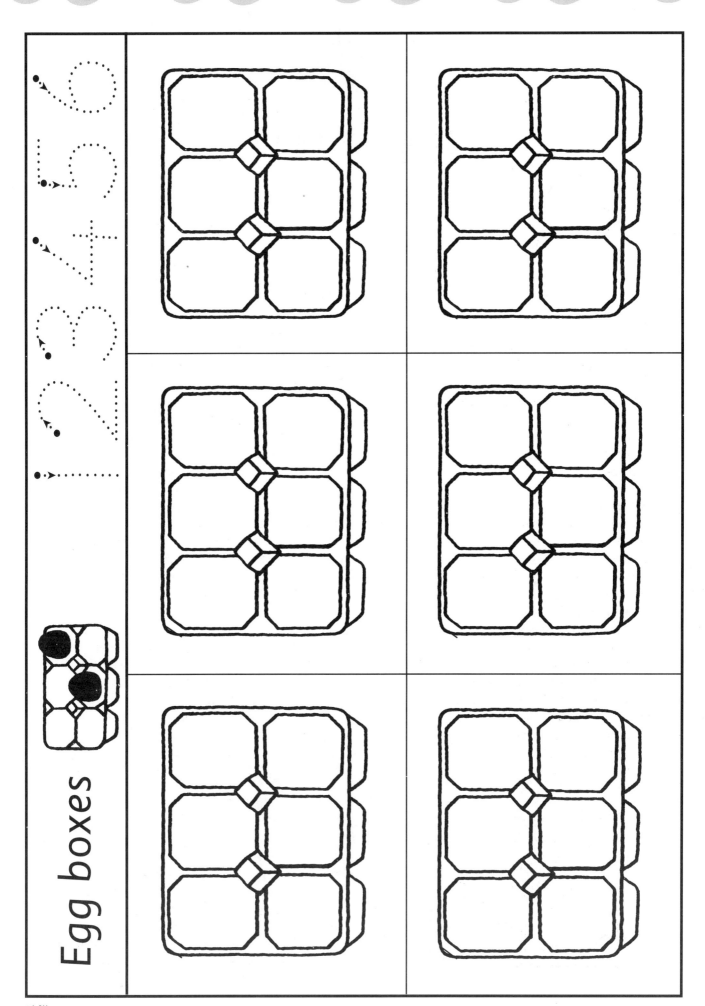

Egg boxes

Spotty dog!

Learning objectives
To practise counting to 7; trace and write the numerals 1 to 7.

Group size
Small groups of four children working with an adult.

What you need
A copy of the photocopiable sheet for each child; four photocopiable sheets copied onto thin card; a six-sided dice marked with three spots and three blanks; a shaker, scissors, glue and spreaders.

Preparation
Laminate the four copies of the photocopiable sheet on thin card to make playing boards. Cut up the strips of spots to make four sets of seven spot cards. Secure each set with an elastic band. Cut the strips of dots from the bottom of the children's sheets.

What to do
Give each child a laminated playing board and a set of seven spot cards. Explain to the children that they are going to play a game called Spotty dog. They must take turns to throw the dice. If they throw a 'spot', then they can take a spot card to put on their dog. If they throw a 'blank', then they cannot take a spot, and must pass the dice on to the next player.

Take some time in between turns to ask the children how many spots they each have on their dog and how many they have left. The first child to place all seven spots on the dog and call out 'Spotty dog!' is the winner of the game.

Individual recording
Give each child a copy of the photocopiable sheet and a strip of spots. Draw the children's attention to the numbers at the top of the sheet and ask them to trace the numbers by placing their pencil on the dot and following the arrows. Invite them to cut the individual spots from the strips and to glue them carefully onto the dog. Let the children work at their own pace. When they have finished, ask them to count the spots on the dog and write the number in the box.

Support
Reduce the number of spot cards for the game and the individual work to the number that children can comfortably count to and recognize as a written numeral.

Extension
Prepare some extra strips of spots. Encourage children to work on the individual activity with a larger number of spots that they can comfortably count to and recognize as a written numeral (up to 10).

Assessment
Note whether the child can play the game correctly. When asked to count the spots, does the child need to touch them individually or can she count them by sight? In the individual activity, note whether the child is able to count the spots and write the number correctly.

Home links
Encourage parents to give their child a set of shuffled playing cards with the cards from aces to sevens. Ask them to help their child sort the cards into seven piles (all the aces, all the twos and so on).

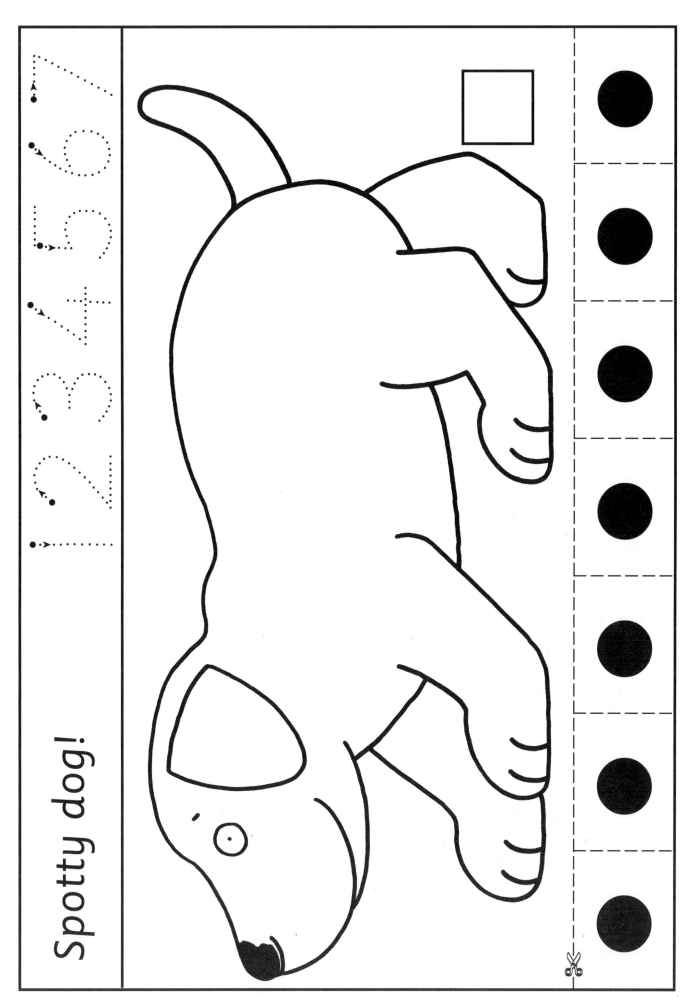

Spotty dog!

Money spider

Learning objectives

To count to 8; to trace the numeral 8; to recognize the eight coins in the money system.

Group size

Four to six children working with an adult.

What you need

A copy of the photocopiable sheet for each child; pencils; black crayons; sets of plastic coins – 1p, 2p, 5p, 10p, 20p, 50p, £1, £2 (up to eight of each coin); coin stamps and stamping pad; eight paper plates.
To make the spiders: cardboard apple tray; black pipe-cleaners; small self-adhesive circles; hole punch; black paint; brushes; sewing needle; strong black cotton or shirring elastic.

Preparation

Cut a hollow half-sphere shape for each child from the apple tray to make the spider's body. Use a hole punch to make eight holes around the edge of each shape, then ask the children to paint the shapes black.

What to do

Tell the children about lucky money spiders, and explain that they are going to make their own money spiders. Give each child a painted spider's body and eight pipe-cleaners. Help them to push the pipe-cleaners through the holes in the body and to secure by twisting the end, then to bend them into leg shapes. Let the children stick on two self-adhesive circles for eyes. Use a sewing needle to thread cotton or elastic through the top of each spider's body. Tie a knot to secure the thread and leave a good length so that the spiders can be hung up.

Wind some black paper around PE hoops then staple strips of black card across to look like a spider's web. Hang the hoops at different heights, then dangle the spiders from them.

Individual recording

Place the coins in the centre of the table with the paper plates in front of them. Ask the children to sort the coins according to type on the plates. Look at each plate and ask the children to name and count the coins. Put all the coins back into a pile, then ask each child to find a particular coin, hold it up and say its name.

Give each child a copy of the photocopiable sheet. Encourage them to trace the numerals, starting at the dots and following the arrows. Now ask them to draw eight legs on the spider. Let each child choose a coin stamp and stamp eight coins at random on the spider's web. Ask them to colour in their picture. Alternatively, let the children draw around a plastic coin. Scribe the value inside in yellow marker pen for the children to trace over.

Support

Stamp or draw around eight 1p coins on each web. Challenge the children to match the 1p coins on the sheet with plastic coins and then count them.

Extension

Ask the children to stamp or draw around one of each type of coin on the spider's web. Scribe the value inside each coin with a yellow marker pen for the children to trace. Ask the children to match the coins on the sheet with plastic coins and then say the name of each coin.

Assessment

Note whether the child can count correctly to 8 and trace numerals correctly. Note whether the child can sort the eight different coins by type and which coins he can identify by name.

Home links

Encourage parents to help their child sort real coins by type and identify the coins by name.

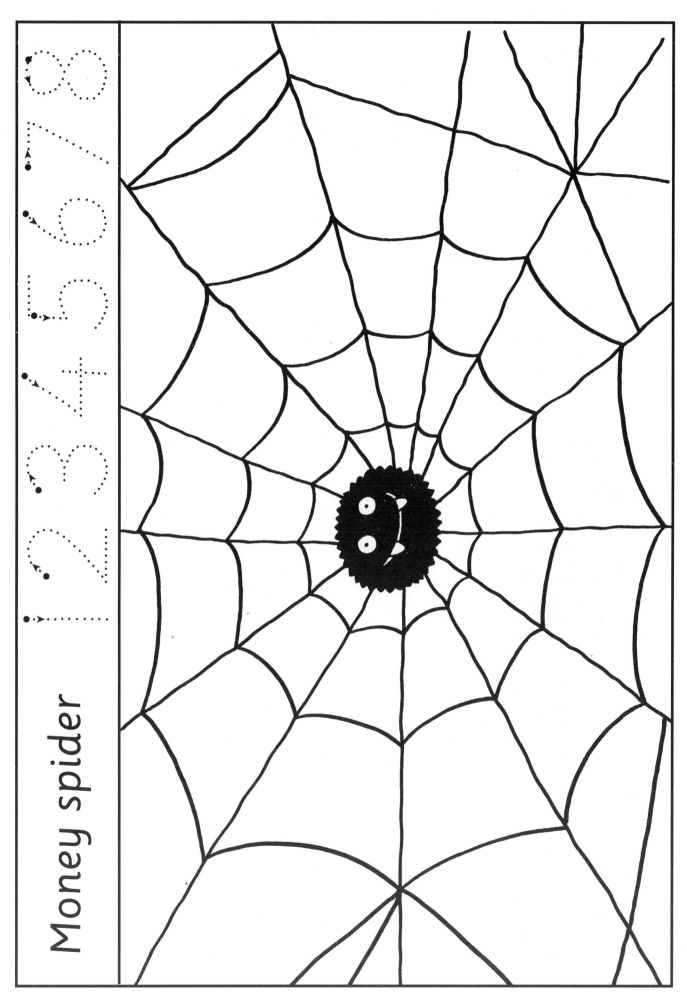

Money spider

12345678

Colour pies

Learning objectives
To make a whole circle with eight segments in various colours; to count the number of segments of the same colour.

Group size
Four children working with an adult.

What you need
Eight brightly-coloured card circles (two red, two blue, two green and two yellow) exactly the same size as the circle on the photocopiable sheet, clearly marked into eight segments and laminated; a copy of the photocopiable sheet for each child; four brightly-coloured paper circles (red, blue, green and yellow) exactly the same size as the circle on the photocopiable sheet; glue and spreaders; pencils.

Preparation
Mark and cut up one of each of the four coloured circles on laminated card into eight separate segments so that you have one complete circle and one set of segments in each colour. Mark and cut up the four coloured paper circles into eight segments. Place them in a separate tray.

What to do
Give each child one of the complete laminated circles. Place the tray of laminated card segments in the centre of the table. Tell the children that they are going to make a special Colour Pie on their circle using the segments of pie in the tray. Invite them to count out eight segments from the tray, making sure they choose a range of colours. Now help them to place all eight segments in position on their circle to make a complete pie. When the children have completed their pies, help each child in turn to count the number of red segments, blue segments and so on.

Individual recording
Give each child a photocopied sheet. Explain that they are going to make an exact copy of their colour pie on the sheet. In turn, show each child the tray of paper slices and help them to sort out the colours they need. Tell them to put the paper slices on the pie in the correct place, using their laminated pies as reference, then to stick each slice into the correct place. When they have completed their pies, ask them to count the number of different-coloured segments, and to write the numbers in the correct boxes on the sheet.

Support
Ask the children to select all of the segments that match their circle in order to complete their pie. Ask 'How many slices altogether?' Help the children to stick segments of the same colour to the pie on the photocopiable sheet.

Extension
When the children have made their pie, ask them to rearrange it so that all slices of the same colour are next to each other. Ask 'Which colour has the most/least slices?' 'Are there any colours with the same number of slices?'

Assessment
Note whether the child can fit the segments together correctly and count the number of slices of the same colour. In the individual recording, note whether the child can match the pie she has made to the one on the sheet. Note whether she can count the number of slices of the same colour and write the numbers correctly in the boxes on the sheet.

Home links
Ask parents to help their child count out eight grapes onto a plate. Take away one grape at a time, saying, 'If one grape is eaten, how many are left?' and so on. Ask them to let their child lay out a plate for each family member and share out the grapes. How many are on each plate?

Colour pies

red

blue

green

yellow

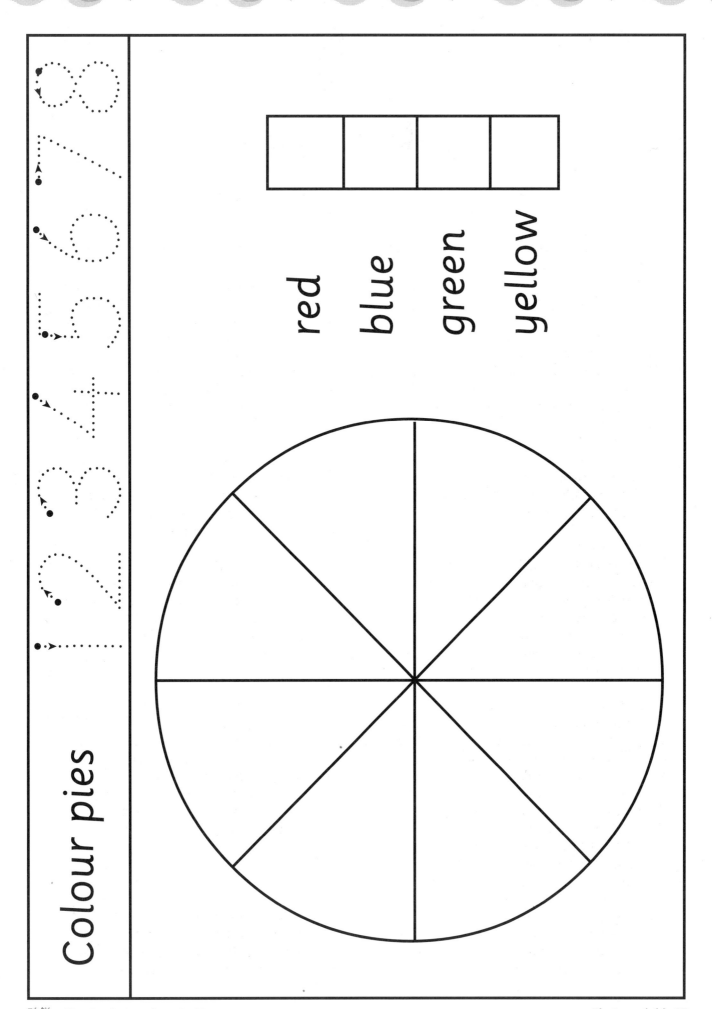

Number eater

Learning objectives
To match objects to numbers 1 to 9; to trace and write numbers 1 to 9.

Group size
Four to six children working with an adult.

What you need
A copy of the photocopiable sheet for each child; A4 card; nine paper plates; a box of cubes or bricks; crayons or felt-tipped pens.

Preparation
Draw and decorate a monster's head on the sheet of A4 card and cut it out. Number the paper plates 1 to 9 with a felt-tipped pen.

What to do
Lay the monster's head on the floor and place the other plates in order behind it to make a body. Sit the children in front of the monster. Show them the box of cubes or bricks. Tell them that the monster is hungry and needs feeding with cubes. Explain that each part of the monster's body needs different amounts of food. Starting at number 1, ask a child to put the correct number of cubes on the plate. Continue along the body, inviting different children to count out and place the correct number of cubes. Ask a different child to check that the number of cubes is correct each time.

Repeat the activity starting at the number 9 and working back to the number 1. Complete the activity by pointing to each plate in turn for the children to count together aloud from 1 to 9 and then back again.

Individual recording
Give each child a copy of the photocopiable sheet and ask them to trace the numerals at the top of the sheet. Now ask them to write the numbers in the boxes on the monster's body in the correct order from 1 to 9. Tell the children that today, the monster wants to eat chocolate buttons, and they must feed it by drawing the correct number of buttons in the space around the squares in each part of its body.

To extend the activity, make a 'Number Eater' display. Make a replica of the plate monster using large paper plates. Invite two or three children to decorate the head with collage materials. Write the numbers 1 to 9 in boxes on the plates, then ask the children to draw or paint the correct number of objects in the spaces around the boxes. Assemble the monster on a wall with the children's sheets around it.

Support
Let the children write numbers as far as they can, then draw chocolate buttons in the parts they have numbered. Let them choose how to colour the remaining parts.

Extension
When they have finished feeding the monster, ask the children to draw some spikes along the monster's back. Encourage them to count the number of spikes and to write the number by the monster's tail on the photocopiable sheet.

Assessment
Note whether the child can write numbers to 9 and match the numbers with objects correctly.

Home links
Encourage parents to read or tell their child the story of *The Very Hungry Caterpillar* by Eric Carle (Puffin), letting their child count the different pieces of food that the caterpillar eats.

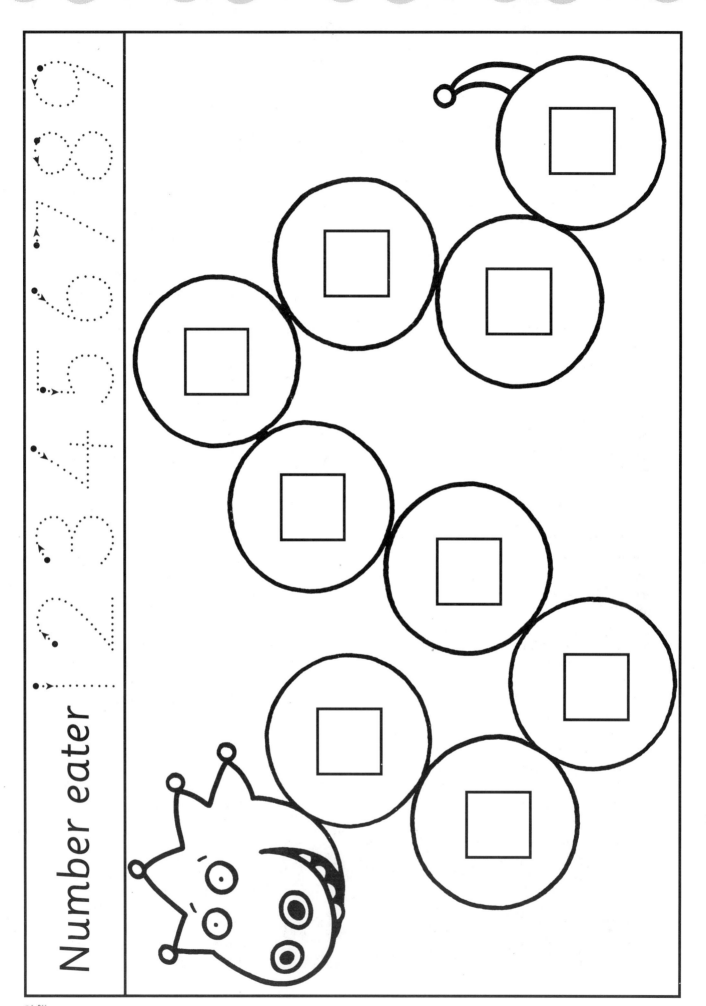

Number eater

Count down

Learning objective
To count down from 10 to 0.

Group size
Whole group game; small group activity for four children working with an adult.

What you need
Four copies of the photocopiable sheet, copied onto card and laminated; ten sheets of green card; marker pen; a dice marked 0, 1, 2, 0, 1, 2; a shaker; ten coloured counters for each child; a spinner numbered 1 to 10 for older children.

Preparation
Cut each piece of card into the shape of a bottle and number them from 1 to 10.

What to do
Sit the children in a semicircle. Ask ten children to stand in a line in front of the group and give each child a bottle card numbered 1 to 10 in order to hold. Sing the song 'Ten Green Bottles', asking each child in the line to sit down at the appropriate place in each verse.

At the end of the song, ask the children in the line to stand up again, then tell them to sit down in turn as all the children count down from 10 to 0 aloud. Repeat the oral countdown, choosing different children to hold up the cards.

Individual task
Give each child a laminated playing board and ten counters. Ask the children to place one counter next to each number on the rocket. Explain that they are going to take turns to throw the dice and to take the number of counters off the board shown by the number on the dice, starting with the counter on the number 10. So, for example, if a 2 is shaken, then the child takes off the counters next to 10 and 9. Take some time between turns to ask the children how many counters are left on their rockets. The first child to remove all their counters calls out 'Blast off!' and is the winner.

Support
Repeat the game in different sessions to increase familiarity.

Extension
Play the game with a spinner marked 1 to 10. Spin the spinner and remove the corresponding counter from the rocket. The first child to remove all the counters is the winner.

Assessment
Note whether the child can count down orally from 10 correctly. During the game, note whether the child can count the counters left by sight or whether he needs to touch each one.

Home links
Encourage parents to help their child at home by using a set of playing cards with the picture cards removed. Sort out two suits. Lay one suit in a line from ten down to the ace. Shuffle the other suit and give the pile of cards to the child. Ask the child to make another line underneath to match the numbers in the first line. As the game becomes more familiar, add another suit and ask the child to make two lines.

Count down

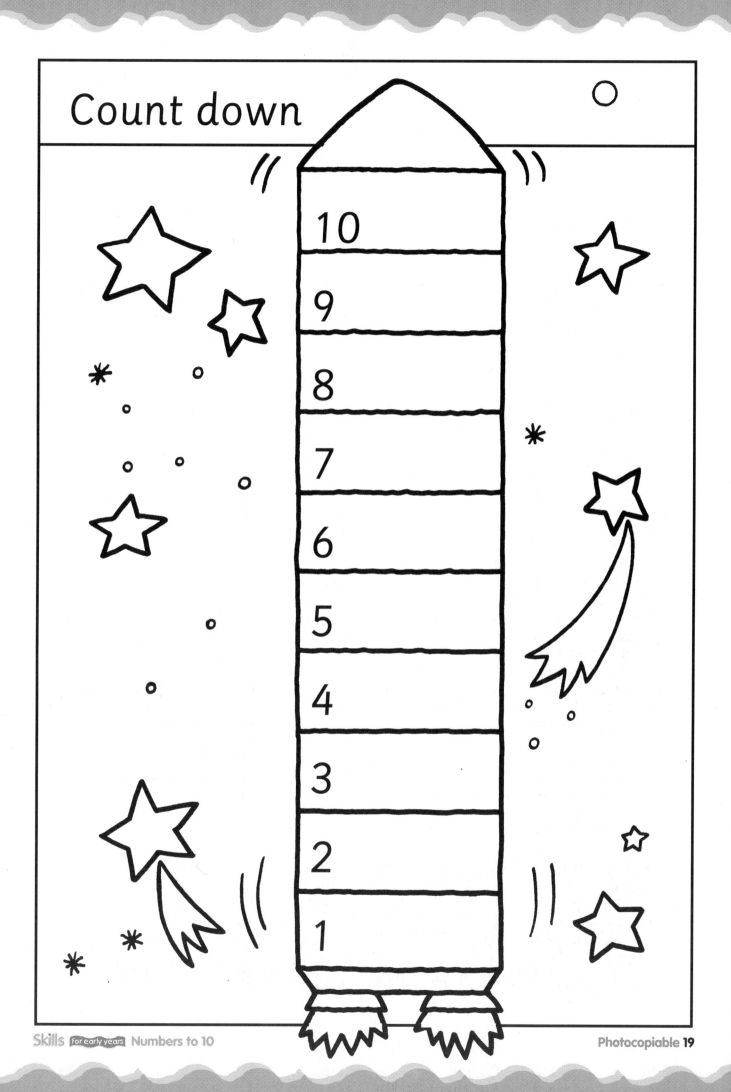

Number hunt

Learning objective

To place and recognize numbers 1 to 10 in the correct order.

Group size

Whole group activity; small group activity for four to six children working with an adult.

What you need

A copy of the photocopiable sheet for each child; ten sheets of plain A4 card; marker pen; washing line; pegs.

Preparation

Using a marker pen, write the numbers from 1 to 10 on the A4 card. Place each card where it can be easily seen in different places around the room. Tie the washing line across a large space in the room.

What to do

Sit the children in a semicircle in front of the washing line. Explain that you have placed numbered cards all around the room and you are going to ask individual children to find a number and peg it on the washing line. Start with the number 1, asking a child to find the card and peg it on the line. Now ask the children to tell you what number comes next before choosing another child to find the number two. Continue until all the cards have been pegged on the line, then invite different children to remove a card from the line and give it to you,

starting at the number 10. Again, ask the children what number comes next before choosing another child to remove the next number.

Individual recording

Give each child a copy of the photocopiable sheet and invite them to join the dots in order, starting at the number 1. Invite them to colour their finished pictures.

Support

Choose the younger children to find the lower number cards around the room (1 to 5). Encourage them to join the numbered dots in order as far as possible themselves on the photocopiable sheet. Finish off the outline in yellow marker for the children to trace and then colour the picture.

Extension

Ask the children to join the dots on the photocopiable sheet starting at the number 10 and counting down to 1.

Assessment

Note whether the child can place and recognize numbers 1 to 10 in the correct order.

Home links

Encourage parents to help their child at home by buying or making a simple dot-to-dot book for their child to complete and colour the pictures.

Number hunt

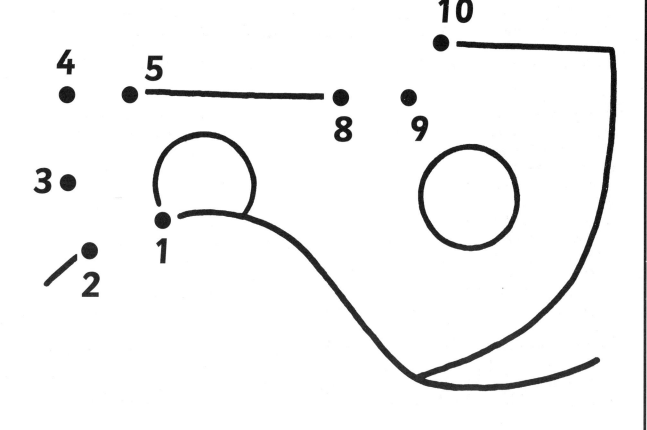

Pairs

Learning objectives

To recognize a pair of objects and begin to add two more to a set.

Group size

Four to six children working with an adult.

What you need

A copy of the photocopiable sheet for each child; five pairs of socks of different colour or pattern; a basket; washing line; pegs; felt-tipped pens or crayons; scissors; glue and spreaders.

Preparation

Cut the strips of socks from the bottom of each photocopiable sheet. Tie the washing line across a large space in the room.

What to do

Start by sitting the children in a semicircle facing the washing line. Place the basket of socks and the pegs in front of the children. Invite a child to find a pair of socks and use two pegs to peg them next to each other on the line. Can the children tell you how many socks are on the line? Repeat the procedure with another child, carrying on until all the socks are on the line in pairs. Each time a pair is added, ask the children to tell you how many socks there are in total.

Now unpeg all the socks and replace them in the basket. Change the activity by asking one child to peg just one sock on the line. Now choose another child to find the matching sock in the basket to peg alongside the first. At each stage, ask the children 'How many socks are on the line now?'.

Individual recording

Give each child a copy of the photocopiable sheet with the separate strip of socks. Ask the children to start by tracing the numbers at the top of the sheet,

placing their pencil on the big dots and following the arrows. Now ask them to cut up the individual sock cards from the strip and colour the socks to make matching pairs. When they have finished, invite them to glue each pair of socks onto one of the washing lines. When the children have completed their sheets, ask them to count how many socks there are altogether and to write the number in the box underneath the washing lines.

Support

Reduce the numbers of pairs of socks to three.

Extension

If children are familiar with counting and writing numbers above 10, use spare strips of socks to give children an extra pair to colour and stick on the line (twelve socks in total).

Assessment

Note whether the child can match pairs of socks correctly and count the total number.

Home links

Encourage parents to help their child at home by collecting together a small box of different socks for their child to put into pairs. Ask parents to encourage their child to count the individual socks as far as they can.

Pairs

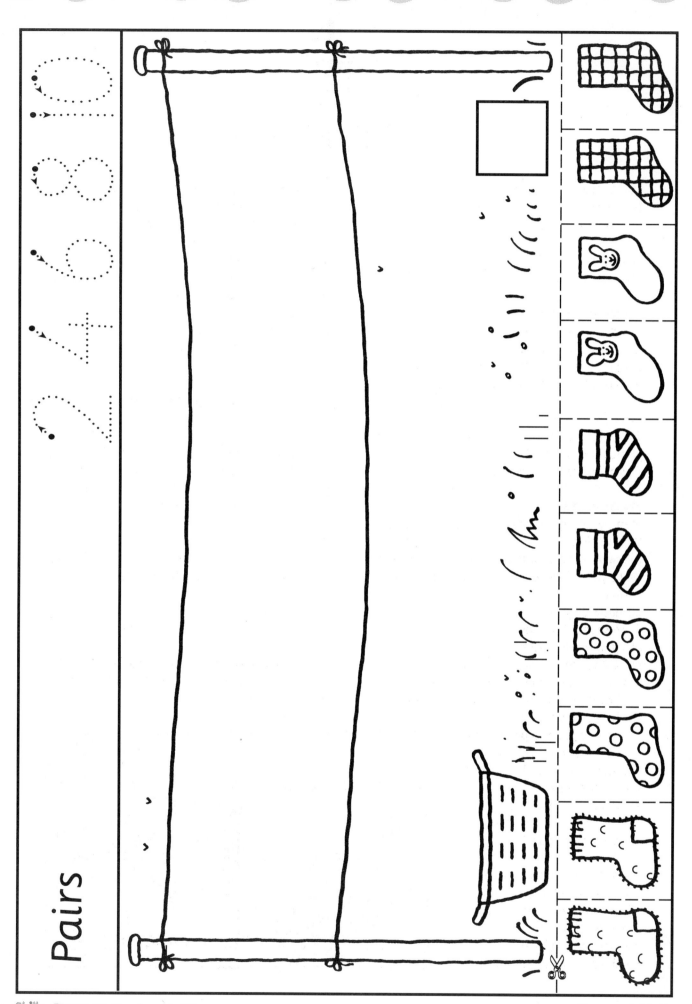

Double up

Learning objectives
To recognize a double number and count the total of double numbers up to double six.

Group size
Four to six children working with an adult.

What you need
A copy of the photocopiable sheet for each child; a set of dominoes; a paper plate; a small tray; pencils; black and red crayons or felt-tipped pens.

What to do
Lay out a set of dominoes on the table face down. Explain to the children that they are going to take turns to pick up a domino. If the numbers of spots are the same on both sides of the domino (or both sides have no spots), they can put it on the plate. If the numbers of spots on both sides of the domino are not the same, then they should put the domino into the tray. When all the dominoes have been sorted, put the tray with the non-matching dominoes to one side.

Lay out all the dominoes from the plate in a line in number order. Tell the children that all of these dominoes are called 'doubles', because both sides of the domino have the same number of spots (or no spots).

Ask each child in turn to pick up one domino and to count the number of spots altogether. Do this a few times so that each child has an opportunity to pick up different dominoes. Collect in the dominoes, mix them up and place them in the centre of the table.

Now ask each child in turn to pick up a specific domino, such as the double two or a double blank.

Individual recording
Give each child a copy of the photocopiable sheet and ask them to look at the ladybirds. Explain that all the ladybirds need a double number of spots. Invite the children to count the number of spots drawn on the first wing, then to use a crayon or felt-tipped pen to draw the same number of spots in the second wing. When they have finished, ask them to count the total number of spots on each ladybird and to write the number in the box. Invite the children to colour the ladybirds.

Support
Let the children work with the ladybirds with spots from one to four. Provide help to count and draw the correct number of spots on the empty wings, then let the children colour in the pictures.

Extension
Add extra spots to the ladybirds' wings. Encourage the children to count and draw the correct number of spots past double six, up to a number that they can comfortably count to.

Assessment
Note whether the child can recognize and count the total of double numbers up to double six. Note which double dominoes the child can count the total by sight, and which dominoes she needs to touch the spots to find the total. Note whether the child can record double numbers using spots and then find the total.

Home links
Ask parents to play dominoes with their child at home to help reinforce the work on doubles.

Double up

Wheels on the bus

Learning objectives
To count and write numbers to 10; to find the total when one more is added to a number.

Group size
Whole group game; small group activity for four to six children working with an adult.

What you need
A copy of the photocopiable sheet for each child; scissors; felt-tipped pens; glue; spreaders; pencils. For the bus: 11 chairs; a small table; a paper plate; a set of ten 1p coins; a hat.

Preparation
Cut the strips of passengers from the children's sheets. Set up two lines of five chairs to represent bus seats. Place the driver's chair and a table at the front. Put the paper plate on the table.

What to do
Explain to the children that they are going to play a game. When passengers get on the bus they must pay the driver a fare of 1p each. Choose ten children to be passengers and give them 1p each. Choose a child to be the driver, and to sit in the driver's seat wearing the hat.

Ask one passenger to board the bus, giving their fare to the driver, who puts it on the plate. Ask the second passenger to do the same. As each passenger boards, ask 'How many passengers are on the bus now?'. Ask the driver 'How much money is on the plate now?'. Continue until all ten passengers have boarded, then sing 'The Wheels On The Bus' together. Repeat the activity, with different children.

Individual recording
Write '1 more' in the 'rule' box on each sheet, then give one sheet to each child, with a strip of passengers. Ask the children to cut out the individual squares, then to stick one passenger in the first window on the bus. Now ask them to stick another passenger next to the first. Look at the boxes on the right, and the '1 more' rule. Say 'There was one passenger on the bus, and one more got on. How many are there now?' Ask them to write the answer in the box on the right. Continue until all passengers have been stuck on, then invite the children to colour the bus.

Mount the completed sheets to make a wall display. Let the children colour in enlarged strips of passengers for a colourful border.

Support
Select a number below ten that children can comfortably count to, recognize and write. Cover the number statements that are not required and reduce the number of passengers.

Extension
Write '1 less' in the rule box. Ask children to place one passenger in each window. Ask them to count the total number of passengers and then to remove one passenger from the bus each time, and complete the boxes on the right.

Assessment
Note whether the child can count, recognize and write all the numbers up to ten and whether he can add one more to a set, then count and record the total.

Home links
Ask parents to count out a number of 1p coins from 1 to 10 with their child. Invite the child to count the coins, then take one more. Now ask the child to count how many coins there are altogether and say the total amount. When the children are confident, ask parents to provide ten 1p coins and repeat the activity where the child takes one coin away each time.

Wheels on the bus

Rule

1
2
3
4
5
6
7
8
9
10

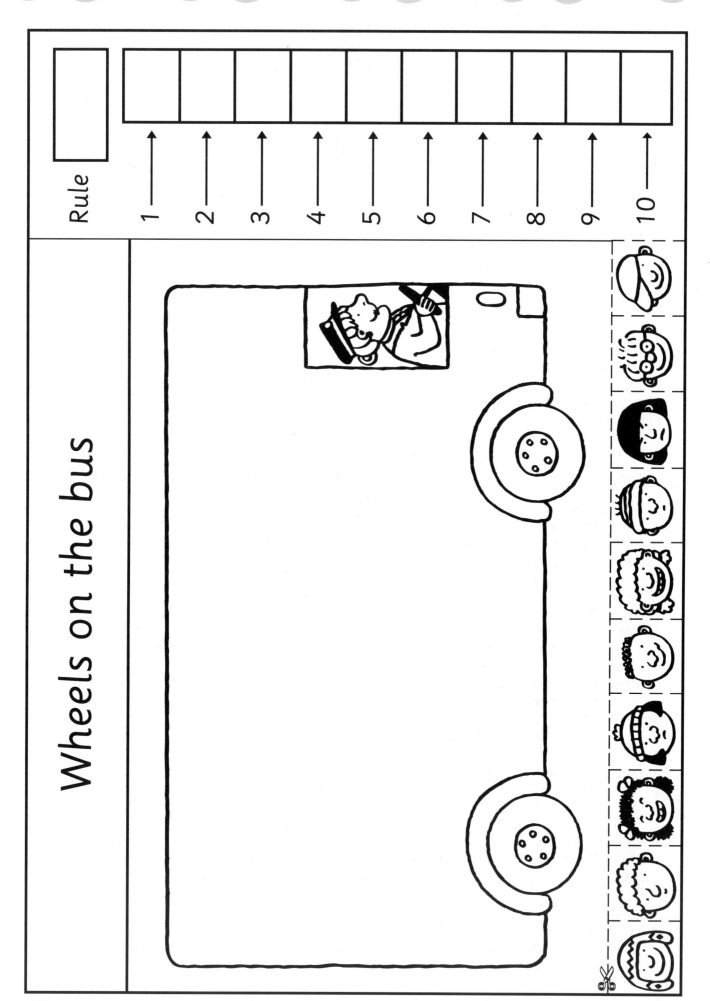

Tellytally

Learning objectives
To collect simple data using tally marks; to count and record totals and say which number is more or less.

Group size
Whole group activity; small group activity for four children working with an adult.

What you need
A copy of the activity sheet for each child plus one copy enlarged to A3 size; small easel; coloured marker pens; four clipboards; pencils and felt-tipped pens.

Preparation
Attach the A3 photocopied sheet to the easel.

What to do
Sit the children in a semicircle and place the easel in front of the group. Talk about children's television programmes. Decide together which are the group's three favourite children's programmes. Using three different-coloured marker pens, colour the outlines of each television a different colour and write the name of each programme, or an associated picture or letter sign, in the same colour on the screen.

Now ask each child in turn to tell you which of the three group favourites is their favourite. For each response, write a tally mark in the appropriate row. When all the children have had a turn, ask them to help you count the total number of tally marks in each row. Write the answer in the box at the end. Talk about the results of the survey. Which programme was the overall favourite? Which was the least favourite?

Individual recording
Set up the easel in front of the group. Ask the children to suggest their favourite cartoon characters, and draw up a shortlist of the three favourites. Give each child a photocopied sheet, clipboard and pencil, and ask them to draw pictures of each character in the screens. In small groups, invite the children to ask the rest of the group which is their favourite character from the three selected, and to make a tally mark to record each vote. When all the children have filled in their sheet, ask them to count the total number of tally marks in each row and write the number in the appropriate box.

Support
Give the children a sheet of paper each to draw a picture of their favourite television character.

Extension
Working in small groups, let the children find out their friends' favourite toys. Again, start by drawing up a short list together, then let the children question their friends, making a tally to show the most popular toy.

Assessment
Note whether children can record tally marks, count the marks and write numbers correctly.

Home links
Ask parents to give their child a tube of coloured sweets. Let the children tip the sweets onto a plate, then sort them into piles according to the different colours. Which pile has the most sweets? Which has the least?

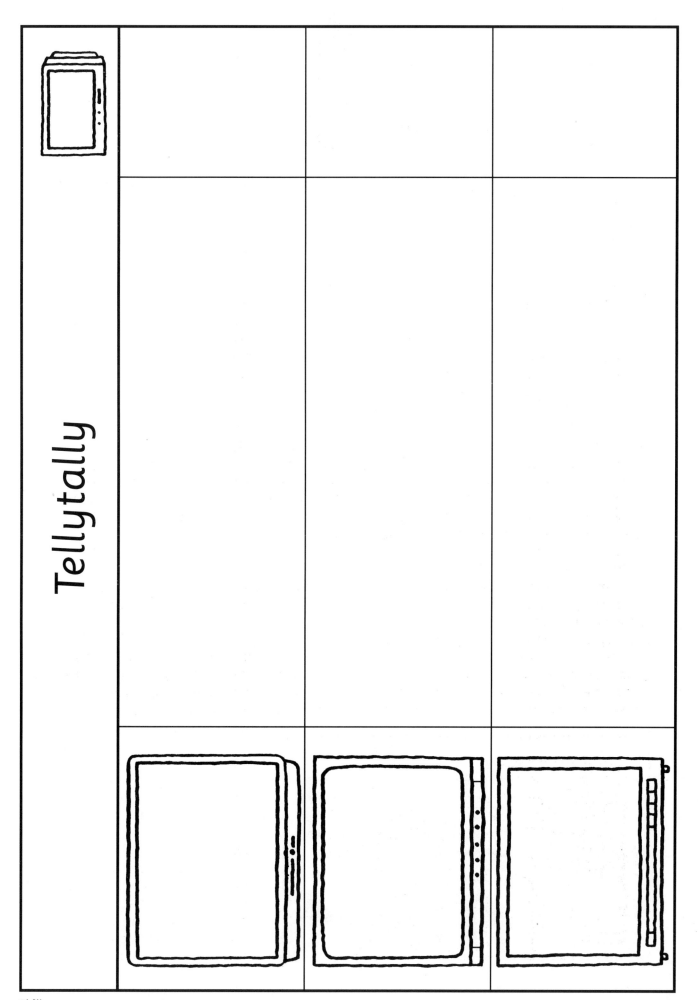

Tellytally

Domino counts

Learning objectives
To count the spots on dominoes and record the total numbers.

Group size
Four to six children working with an adult.

What you need
A copy of the photocopiable sheet for each child plus one enlarged copy to A3 size; felt-tipped pens or crayons; pencils; a set of dominoes; small easel; marker pen.

Preparation
Attach the enlarged photocopiable sheet to the easel.

What to do
Start by laying all the dominoes face down on the table. Ask the children to each pick up a domino.
Now ask each child in turn to count and say the number of spots on each side of their domino. For example 'Three and two makes five'. Continue the activity until there are no dominoes left on the table.

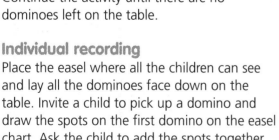

Individual recording
Place the easel where all the children can see and lay all the dominoes face down on the table. Invite a child to pick up a domino and draw the spots on the first domino on the easel chart. Ask the child to add the spots together

and write the total number in the space beside the domino. Repeat this until each child has taken a turn to use the chart.
Give each child a copy of the photocopiable sheet and ask them to repeat the activity. Let them take turns to select a domino then to draw the spots on the blank shapes on their sheet. Repeat until all the blank dominoes are completed.

Support
Use only the dominoes that have spots totalling five or less.

Extension
Ask the children to write a number sentence about each domino in the space underneath, once they have completed it, for example: 3 and 2 → 5.

Assessment
Note the dominoes on which the child needs to count the spots by touching them to find the total, and the dominoes on which the child is able to add the spots together in her head. Note whether the child has copied the spots correctly onto the sheet and whether she is able to write the total number correctly.

Home links
Invite parents to help their child draw domino shapes on a sheet of paper then to draw in the spots and write the total number beside each domino.

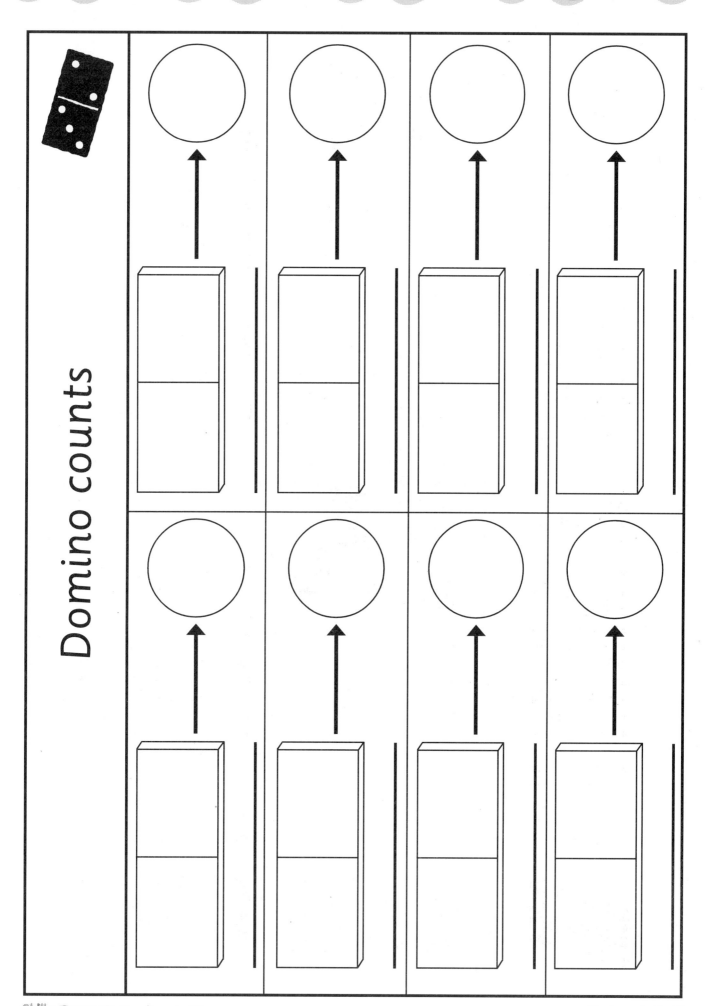

Domino counts

Name _____

Skills development chart

I can count to ☐

I can write numbers correctly to ☐

I can count the spots on one domino and write the number

I can count double numbers to ☐

I can recognize coins by colour and name

I can add one more object to a group of objects and count how many altogether

I can match pairs of objects and count the pairs

I can take one object from a group of objects and count how many are left

I can count a set of two objects without touching

I can count objects up to 10

I can match numbers to objects up to 10

I can write numbers to 10 correctly

I can recognize and count all the spots on a dice